The Jurassic Coast - *Illust*

by Robert Westwood

ISBN 978-0-9552061-8-4

Inspiring Places Publishing
2, Down Lodge Close
Alderholt
Fordingbridge
SP63JA
e-mail robert.westwood3@btinternet.com
www.inspiringplaces.co.uk

Contents

Page

Above: A small waterfall on the beach at Osmington Mills
Right: Looking west from Durdle Door towards Swyre Head and Bat's Head

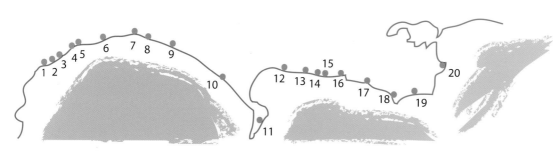

Front cover:
Looking east towards Bat's Head.
Rear cover top:
Rocks near Orcombe Point
Bottom:
Cliffs near Kimmeridge

Introduction

England's only natural World Heritage Site, the 95 miles of the Jurassic Coast provides detailed and fascinating evidence of the history of the planet over 185 million years. This vast time spans three geological periods, the Triassic, Jurassic and Cretaceous and was a crucial era for the development of life on Earth.

If you were able to view a satellite image of the Earth 250 million years ago at the start of the Triassic period, you might not recognise your home planet. The familiar shape of the continents would not be there, instead you would see mostly ocean with one huge landmass, a supercontinent that geologists have named Pangaea. The Earth had recently undergone a huge trauma resulting in around 95% of species being wiped out. The causes of this global extinction are still debated; slow, natural changes in climate and sea level may have

been partly responsible but some sort of catastrophic event such as an asteroid collision or particularly violent volcanic activity is thought likely. In the 185 million years that followed life recovered and flourished before another catastrophe, this time almost certainly an asteroid impact, devastated life again. The course of evolution was dramatically changed, dinosaurs no longer dominated the land and ammonites no longer thrived in the oceans, and the scene was set for the emergence of mammals and thus eventually humans.

The cliffs of East Devon and Dorset provide the world's most important record of life in this era, as it is only from the fossil record that scientists have pieced together a history of life on the planet. Not only that, the rocks provide a history of the changing nature of the Earth's surface and a means of deciphering the processes that have shaped it. If the shape and distribution of the continents have changed over geological time then it is clear huge forces are involved. Scientists think that the hot interior of the Earth, powered by the decay of radioactive elements, drives huge convection currents which in turn provide the energy to move continents when they reach the surface.

View across Sidmouth

The Earth's crust is split into a number of "plates" which slowly move, sometimes colliding, sometimes grating past one another. At other boundaries, always on the ocean floor, plates are moving apart, pushed aside by the constant injection of molten rock, another product of the heating from below. Volcanoes and earthquakes are the everyday reminders of these colossal forces to people who live on or close to the plate boundaries.

In the rocks of the Jurassic Coast we have a record of these plate movements and of the changing shape of the continents. During this time Dorset and East Devon were often near plate boundaries, for example near the split when the great continent of Pangaea began to break up. The faults and folds in the rocks are all evidence of these great earth movements, as is the fact the rocks of the Jurassic Coast were largely deposited on the sea bed; they are marine sediments. It is subsequent earth movements that have raised the compressed and hardened layers above sea level where they are subject to the forces of erosion. Washed by rivers back into the sea the individual grains of sediment may find themselves deposited, compressed and raised again. It is this everlasting cycle that has created the Earth's landscape and the movement of crustal plates has played a major part.

The words and pictures of this book hopefully spread some light on these processes to the interested layman so that the landscape can be looked at with increased understanding and wonder, and its beauty better appreciated.

Note: Opposite each title is the grid reference of where the photograph on the opposite page was taken.

Looking across Kimmeridge Bay

Orcombe Point

SX 023797

Orcombe Point is officially the beginning of the Jurassic Coast World Heritage Site. The "geoneedle" on top of the cliffs marks the spot and represents the variety of rocks found along the 95 mile coast. Fittingly, the oldest rocks of the site are found here, dating from the very bottom of the Triassic period. Although the rocks to the west from the previous Permian period are very similar and from similar environments, the division between the Permian and the Triassic, about 250 million years ago, is an important geological boundary as it marks the time when a major extinction of species took place. Around 95% of all marine species died out and 70% of vertebrates.

It is difficult to piece together the sequence of events and it may be that gradual climate change and one or more catastrophic events played a part. There is no doubt, however, that the creation, through the random movement of the Earth's crustal plates, of one giant supercontinent had major environmental consequences. As well as meaning there were fewer shelf sea habitats, the interior of Pangaea became a vast arid desert. This is where we pick up the story of the rocks at Orcombe Point.

Playa lakes [from the Spanish word for beach] are a common feature of arid or semi-arid regions around the world. These are temporary lakes, often in intermontane [between mountains] basins, which fill up in rainy times and dry out subsequently. The Aylesbeare mudstones and sandstones at Orcombe were formed in such lakes. Some of the sandstones show current bedding [see article on Ladram Bay] which perhaps indicates they formed as desert dunes during dry periods.

The rock layers or strata at Orcombe dip gently to the east, and so as we go along the coast we see younger rocks which lie on top of these very early Triassic layers. If you are there at low tide notice the ledges of sandstone that lead out to sea. These, of course, are the edges of the harder sandstone layers in the cliffs, visible because of the tilt of the strata. Finally at Orcombe look out for small faults in the cliffs, planes of weakness where the rocks have fractured, one side dropping down relative to the other.

A fault in the cliffs near Orcombe

Cliffs near Orcombe Point

Budleigh Salterton

SX 067818
SX 057815 -below

As we travel eastwards from Orcombe Point to Budleigh Salterton, forwards in geological time, we see more of the sandstones and mudstones formed in shallow lakes and arid deserts. At Budleigh Salterton however, something dramatic happens. In the cliffs west of the town the famous Budleigh Salterton Pebble Beds are exposed. As their name suggests this is a rock formation packed with hard, smooth pebbles.

The pebbles are made from quartzite, a very hard type of sandstone that has been metamorphosed. The quartz grains have been welded together by heat and pressure, typically in the deformations associated with mountain building. The pebbles were brought here by fast flowing rivers coming from mountains to the south from what is now Brittany. There was no English Channel separating the areas then! That the rivers were fast flowing is perhaps obvious from the size of the pebbles. The beach at Budleigh Salterton is made up of pebbles from the eroded Pebble Beds.

It is not difficult to spot this rock formation in the cliffs to the west of the beach, partly because it stops so abruptly. The cliffs seem to be made of two distinct layers. The lower one is the Pebble Beds while above it is more desert sandstone, made increasingly conspicuous because of the "honeycomb" weathering. The junction is very clear, it seems the rivers stopped flowing and the region returned, once more, to dry, desert conditions. It is odd that this interlude should end with a relatively sudden return to previous conditions.

Right: The top of the Pebble Beds can clearly be seen.
Far right: The beach at Budleigh Salterton

Ladram Bay

SY 097851

Ladram Bay is a charming cove carved out of red Otter Sandstone with prominent sea-stacks marking a previous position of the coastline. Sea-stacks form when the sea exploits a weakness in the cliffs, eventually eroding an arch. When the roof of the arch inevitably collapses, an isolated column or stack is left. At Ladram Bay faults and joints are relatively common and this may account for the proliferation of stacks at this location.

The Otter Sandstone is a Triassic formation about 230-240 million years old. In this part of the world the climate was arid or semi-arid and the sandstones were deposited by great rivers flowing south to north in wide, shallow channels. The flow of the rivers would have been very variable. In the cliffs at Ladram Bay geologists can make out the deposits of river channels which shifted position over time, eventually building up over 200 metres of sediment over a wide area.

Here we see a typical feature of relatively coarse grained sediments that have been laid down by currents of either water or wind – current or cross-bedding. Look closely at the cliffs and you can see it almost anywhere at Ladram Bay; layers in the sandstone that are inclined and seem to cut across one another. Imagine the gradual build up of sand on the inside of a long, lazy meander on a broad, shallow river. The sand would be gently inclined from almost the top of the river bank to the bed of the river. We know that river channels are not static; they migrate and meanders are cut off into ox-bow lakes. Sometime later sand may be deposited on top of and at an angle to our original deposit. As this goes on and on the layers, when viewed in cross-section, will produce the patterns we see in the cliffs today. These patterns will also give us information about the direction of the ancient currents and this is how we know the rivers flowed from south to north.

Current bedding in Otter Sandstone

Ladram Bay

Sidmouth

Sidmouth is a pretty seaside resort echoing a time when the affluent came to enjoy the sea air and the wonderful scenery. Part of its charm lies in the many Georgian and Regency buildings which grace the town and the sea front, but its setting between spectacular red cliffs is perhaps its crowning glory.

To the east and west of the town the cliffs are mainly made of Mercian Mudstone. This lies on top of the older Otter Sandstone and marks a return to playa lake type conditions where muds were deposited in a large, shallow, ephemeral lake in a semi-arid desert. This contrasts with the Otter Sandstone which was deposited by large rivers. The town itself lies on the sandstone, a fact explained by faulting which has dropped the mudstone down on the western side of the town. Once again the strata are gently inclined to the east and the junction between the sandstone and mudstone is in the cliffs to the east of the town To the west, therefore, the cliffs would be sandstone if there had been no faulting.

The eastern end of the esplanade is a good place to appreciate and understand one of the key features of the Jurassic Coast, the so called "Great Unconformity". Look along the dramatic line of red cliffs and you should be able to pick out the strata dipping gently to the east. The layers deposited in the ancient playa lake would have been horizontal, subsequent earth movements have tilted these rocks. Note also that these red rocks are all from the Triassic period. Now look towards the top of the cliffs and you will see a much lighter coloured rock; look closely and you may notice that the layers are not inclined anymore but are roughly horizontal. What's more, these rocks are Cretaceous in age, in this locality rocks from the entire Jurassic period are missing. This is what is known as an unconformity and such features are often recognised by disparate strata.

An unconformity represents a period of time when a particular area was subject to erosion rather than deposition, in other words was above sea level. It is not that Jurassic rocks were never deposited here rather that earth movements raised this part of Devon and Dorset above sea level and the landscape was eroded flat. When the sea returned in the Cretaceous more sediments were laid down in horizontal layers. Later earth movements have lifted all the layers above sea level. So, one of the major features in the rocks of the Jurassic Coast is notable for the complete absence of rocks of Jurassic age!

Looking east from the promenade at Sidmouth.

Hooken Cliff

SY 224880

Walking from Beer to Branscombe you are faced with a choice at Hooken Cliff, keep to the top of the cliffs or descend towards sea level on a winding path through what seems like a magical, secret garden. This is the site of the Hooken landslip where, one night in March 1790, huge sections of chalk slipped towards the sea extending the shoreline by about 200 yards.

The explanation for this massive landslide is quite simple and it is a pattern that is repeated all along the Jurassic Coast. Porous rock, in this case the Chalk, lies on top of impermeable strata, here Triassic mudstones. Note the complete absence of the Jurassic! The Cretaceous Chalk lies unconformably on top of the Triassic rocks. This is the Great Unconformity we met at Sidmouth; millions of years of erosion have removed the Jurassic sediments.

As the water percolates through the chalk it meets the impermeable mudstones and spreads out, forming a well lubricated layer deep in the cliffs. Since the strata dip gently out seawards it is unsurprising that, given enough lubrication, chunks simply slide off. In 1790 a huge fissure opened up behind the cliff edge shortly before the landslip. It is estimated that 7-10 acres of land slipped more than 200 feet. The landslip created a reef offshore and lobster pots sunk by fishermen were raised 15 feet above water!

An interesting feature of the rocks in this locality is the tremendous lateral variation in the thickness of some of the strata. In the vicinity of Hooken Cliff the Chalk and other deposits thin considerably. Geologists have interpreted this as showing that the depth of the ancient sea was controlled by fault lines.

This part of the Jurassic Coast illustrates just how important a factor geology is in shaping our landscape. Inland the hilltops trace the extent of the resistant Chalk, while steep valleys reflect the more readily eroded mudstones beneath. Just east of Beer the Chalk abruptly gives way to the red desert mudstones which have been thrust upwards along a fault plane so that they are now level with the much younger Cretaceous strata.

Opposite: The great Hooken landslip

Beer and Seaton

SY 229889
SY 235895 - below

We saw at the start of the Jurassic Coast how the layers of sedimentary rocks or strata are gently inclined eastwards. If this pattern were to be repeated uninterrupted along the coast we would expect to find progressively younger rocks as we work our way eastwards. As a general rule this is what happens – the rocks do indeed get younger towards the other end of the Jurassic Coast at Handfast Point. As you have probably guessed however, things are not quite that simple!

Approaching the pretty fishing village of Beer along the coast path from Seaton, one is struck by the sudden juxtaposition of red Triassic mudstones with the gleaming white Cretaceous Chalk. The actual junction is obscured by landslides at Seaton Hole but it is another fault or plane of weakness caused by tension in the Earth's crust. The younger Chalk would originally have been considerably higher in the rock succession but has been dropped down along the fault, bringing it level with the mudstones. Inland the line of the fault is marked by a valley, often the case as rivers and streams will exploit a line of weakness.

There is another interesting structure along this stretch of coast but it is not so easily appreciated. The Cretaceous rocks here which, remember, lie unconformably on the Triassic, are folded into a gentle syncline or downwards facing fold. The valley in which Beer is built lies along the axis of this syncline, another example of how the structure of the rocks affects the topography.

Finally, at Beer, mention must be made of the famous Beer Stone, an excellent building stone whose former quarries are now a tourist attraction. It can be seen as a thin layer at the foot of the cliffs on Beer beach. This rock corresponds to the Lower Chalk elsewhere and is a good example of how local variations in ancient environments can lead to a different type of rock forming.

Far right: Looking towards Seaton from the path to Beer Head.
Right: The valley shows the line of the fault.

Lyme Regis

SY 335915

Settlement at Lyme Regis goes back to at least the 8th century when monks from an abbey there made salt from seawater. By the 13th century it had grown to be an important port and an artificial harbour, the Cobb, was constructed. Since then it has had a colourful history; it was besieged by Royalists in the Civil War and was the landing place for the Duke of Monmouth in 1685 at the start of his ill judged campaign to take the throne. In the early 19th century a young woman from the town named Mary Anning gained fame as the country's leading fossil collector. Inspired by her father who had died early leaving the family destitute, Mary built up a profitable business and earned the respect of the scientific community. It was she who discovered the first complete skeletons of an Ichthyosaur and a Plesiosaur, now prized exhibits at the Natural History Museum. At this time there was great interest in the "new" science of geology and much debate about how new findings fitted in with the traditional biblical view of the development of life.

The importance of the fossil record in the cliffs of Lyme Regis can hardly be overstated. The blue/grey clays and limestones are from the Lower Jurassic. It was a time when the great continent of Pangaea had begun to break up and Dorset was on the edge of the embryonic Atlantic Ocean. Life flourished in these warm waters that covered the previous desert landscape. The break up of the supercontinent created new environments, driving evolution ever faster. Evidence for the abundance of life comes not just from the conspicuous fossils scattered over the beach by the frequent landslips. The blue/grey colour of the sediments is testament to the anoxic or reducing conditions of the ancient seabed caused by the large amount of organic matter. The most prized ammonite fossils are those preserved as fool's gold or iron pyrites. This mineral is easily produced by organic matter decomposing in the presence of iron. That there are so many of them is again indicative of waters teeming with life.

Opposite: Monmouth Beach, Lyme Regis Right: Ammonite on the beach

Charmouth

SY 365929 - main
SY 393924 - inset

To the west of the mouth of the River Char lies Black Ven cliff, the site of the biggest coastal mudslide complex in Europe. The principal causes behind the frequent slides are not hard to discover. Once again we meet the Great Unconformity, with permeable Cretaceous sands overlying the impermeable clays and marls of the Lower Jurassic. Water that percolates through the Cretaceous sequence lubricates the junction with the clays; combine this with the gentle southerly dip of the plane of the unconformity and we have a perfect recipe for landslides. The strata of the Jurassic clays also dip gently seawards and this further facilitates slides.

The Lower Jurassic rocks are collectively known as the Lias, after the alternating bands of limestone and shale. This is a further example of the rhythmical sedimentation we see at Kimmeridge, probably produced by environmental change caused by the cyclical variation in the tilt of the Earth's axis. For this factor to be apparent indicates a period of otherwise relative quiet. On a larger time scale this was certainly not the case. The Atlantic Ocean was beginning to form and Dorset was in the middle of the action. The stresses and strains in the crust led to much faulting and different basins of deposition formed in the new ocean controlled by these faults. The sea level changed accordingly, sometimes shallow, sometimes deeper. This is confirmed by following the Jurassic strata north from the Dorset coast where they soon begin to thin dramatically. The remains of the flying reptiles [and land dinosaurs] that have been found around Charmouth and Lyme Regis indicate that land was never far away.

As we saw at Lyme Regis, the clays of the Lias are rich in organic matter, a legacy of the profusion of life in the Jurassic oceans. One layer in the cliffs at Charmouth, the "Shales-with-Beef", is particularly rich. The "beef" comes from fibrous deposits of the mineral calcite which formed as the sediment was buried and compacted. Further east this sequence of sediments is deeply buried and consequently has been heated. This has led to the formation of considerable oil deposits which are exploited at the Wytch Farm oilfield in Poole Harbour.

Opposite main: Looking towards Lyme Regis from Charmouth beach.
Opposite inset: Looking towards Charmouth from the cliffs above St. Gabriel's Mouth.

Burton Beach

The dramatic sandstone cliffs of Burton Beach are different to those of east Devon in that they are of marine rather than continental origin. Their colour may have inspired many a photographer to capture the wonderful golden glow as the sun sets, but scrape away the surface and the sandstone is actually a blue/grey colour inside. The familiar orange is produced by surface oxidation.

We have seen sandstones at many places on the Jurassic Coast, but how many people stop to think what sandstone actually is. The descriptions in this book largely focus on the "big picture", how the plates of the Earth's crust have moved, opening and closing oceans and pushing up chains of mountains, how great layers of sediments have formed in different environments. Let's look for a moment at the smaller scale, and consider the profound meaning in William Blake's famous line "To see a world in a grain of sand…".

Sandstone is defined as a sediment with grains between about 1/16mm and 2mm in diameter. The grains are of a number of different minerals, but usually predominantly quartz. Quartz is a very hard mineral and difficult to break down, so when an igneous [volcanic] rock is weathered, the quartz remains intact, merely being eroded into smaller pieces by mechanical means. We should not be surprised quartz is so common, it is a compound of silicon and oxygen, the two most abundant elements in the Earth's crust.

Take a look at a few grains of sand in your hand. You should be able to pick out the clear or milky grains of quartz, perhaps with some darker minerals as well. These may be feldspars, another hard mineral common in igneous rocks. The presence of other minerals can shed light on where and how the sandstone was formed, as can the shape of the grains. The red colour of most sandstones comes from the oxidised iron in the cement that binds the sediment together.

Being quite coarse grained sandstones are typically formed close to the shore, it is usually only the finer grains of silt and clay that are carried into deeper water.

Opposite: Burton Beach

Chesil Beach

SY 555848

At other locations on the Jurassic Coast we have been looking at rocks and structures that formed millions of years ago; here at Chesil Beach we have a feature of the landscape that was only fully developed around 5 000 years ago. It is a useful reminder that the end of the Ice Ages saw dramatic changes to the landscape of Britain in very recent times geologically speaking.

Chesil Beach has been formed by the process known as "longshore drift", where the prevailing direction of the waves takes material along the shoreline, in this case eastwards. As the sea level rose after the last ice melted around 15-20 000 years ago, huge quantities of sandy material were eroded from the area of Lyme Bay and driven onshore, forming a barrier beach. As sea levels continued to rise this beach was pushed further north and east. Much of the material may originally have come from the great meltwater rivers that flowed southwards from the ice sheet during glacial periods. Some recent research concludes that the beach and the Fleet behind it were fully formed around 7-5 000 years ago, but composed of predominantly sandy material. Old cliffs in east Devon which had been stranded by falling sea levels during the Ice Age, now came into the grip of the sea again, resulting in much coarse gravel being washed away. This was transported eastwards and covered Chesil Beach with the pebbles we see today. This material has now been exhausted and is one of the reasons why Chesil Beach is very vulnerable to environmental changes.

An enduring mystery surrounds the distribution and size of the pebbles. The further east you go on the beach, the larger the size of the pebbles, ranging from pea size at West Bay to large cobbles near Portland. Legend has it that local smugglers could tell exactly where they were on the beach at night by the size of the pebbles. It has been suggested that the larger pebbles are carried further by the currents because of their greater surface area.

Chesil Beach from Portland

Chesil Beach near Abbotsbury

The Isle of Portland

SY 693704

Joined only to the mainland by the shingle of Chesil Beach, the Isle of Portland is a unique and special place. It is the type area for the Portland Beds, part of the uppermost sequence of fossil rich Jurassic rocks. Viewed from above Portland looks like a great slab of limestone sloping gently southwards. The strata here are the southern part of a great fold or anticline, similar to the structure we have met in the Isle of Purbeck and again formed at the time of the great Alpine earth movements.

The oldest rock on Portland is the Kimmeridge Clay which can be seen underlying the Portland series on the north of the isle. These then pass into the Portland Sand, the Portland Stone and finally the Purbeck Beds, a sequence which represents a gradual shallowing of the Jurassic sea. The rocks on Portland have been extensively studied because they provide much information about the changing environments in this ancient ocean and about the creatures that lived in them.

The limestones on Portland are mainly of a type known as oolites. These are composed of tiny spherical grains of calcium carbonate cemented together. They are known to form in very shallow, high energy environments where the rolling action of the waves encourages tiny sand particles or shell fragments to become concentrically coated in calcium carbonate. [see section on Seacombe] Near Portland Bill it is very easy to spot the many thousands of fossilised oyster shells, another indicator that this was a very shallow sea.

As we pass through the Portland beds to the Purbeck series the rocks indicate a further shallowing of the sea to the point when we have the lagoonal conditions that led to the freshwater limestones of the Purbeck formation. All through this time the variations of sea level were controlled by the movements of tectonic plates. There are indications that these changes sometimes happened quickly, for example the fossilised remains of tree stumps.

The landscape of Portland has not just been shaped by nature but also by the extensive quarrying of Portland Stone, claimed to be the world's best building stone. The census of 1851 recorded that over one fifth of the male population was engaged in the trade. Demand for the stone has now largely vanished and the abandoned quarries in the cliffs are ideal places for geological field trips!

Old quarries at Cheyne Weare on Portland

Osmington Mills

SY 734817

Osmington Mills is a tiny hamlet east of Weymouth. Although just a scattered settlement of a few houses, it boasts a charming, well-known pub the Smugglers' Inn. In the late 18th and early 19th centuries this was a major smuggling centre and the inn was the base of a notorious smuggler known as "French Peter". Formerly called "The Crown", the inn adopted its present name, its usual nickname, in the 1970s.

A range of typical Jurassic rocks are to be seen at Osmington Mills. Clays, sandstones and limestones from the warm, shallow seas are all to be found here. The visitor really can appreciate the importance of the principle of "uniformitarianism", first propounded by Charles Lyell in the 1830s. He felt that the processes operating on the Earth's crust today have done so throughout geological time and that gradual change is the key factor. Before this many practitioners of the new science of geology believed that catastrophic events had formed and shaped the landscape, notably the biblical flood.

At Osmington we again see an oolitic limestone [see articles on Portland and Seacombe] formed from compacted calcareous sediment of the type currently accumulating in shallow, tropical, high-energy environments. A little east of the slipway you may see a formation known as the Bencliff Grit. Examine it closely and look for ripples formed on the bed of a shallow Jurassic sea, for the burrows of worms and for cross-bedding indicative of the changing ancient currents. All these features can be seen in marine sediments accumulating on the sea floor today, and together they help us build a picture of what the Jurassic oceans were like and how they changed over time.

The rocks here at Osmington are from the Oxfordian age of the Upper Jurassic and are around 155 million years old. In Britain part of the Oxfordian succession is known as the Corallian, from the abundance of fossil corals. It is interesting to note that scientists have calculated that at this time Dorset was over 50° north of the equator, while present day corals are restricted to a belt 30° either side of the equator. Assuming corals then required much the same conditions as they do today, either the world's climate was a lot warmer then or the equator was much further north.

Limestones at Osmington Mills

Bat's Head

SY 795804

Chalk gives the name to the geological period it was formed in. Cretaceous comes from the Latin "creta" meaning chalk. This period followed immediately on from the Jurassic, beginning around 140 million years ago and lasting for approximately 75 million years. Early in this period, southern Britain was on the edge of a continent and rocks from this time show evidence that they were formed in a huge river delta. Later on the sea seems to have returned and marine rocks such as sandstones are found. Then conditions changed; Dorset was covered by a warm, shallow sea where very little mud, silt or sand collected. How could this be? Was land far away or was the sea surrounded by waterless deserts where there were no rivers to wash sediment into it? The scene was set for the formation of a remarkable rock that now seems so familiar and prosaic.

Then, as now, this warm sea was bursting with life: the fossil record has shown us many species that flourished in the nutrient rich waters. At the bottom of the food chain lie the microscopic photosynthesising organisms that must proliferate in vast numbers to supply the larger animals and maintain their own existence. One such organism is the coccolithophore, a type of phytoplankton. This clever creature precipitates dissolved calcium carbonate from sea water and uses it to make small protective plates. Each one covers itself with up to 30 of the plates which are typically about three thousandths of a millimetre in diameter. When the organism dies they detach and sink to the bottom of the ocean. Modern scanning electron microscopes allow us to look in detail at these minute shields and they are staggeringly beautiful – each one looking as if it has been carved by a master craftsman.

Coccolithophores carry on today much as they did in Cretaceous times. In parts of the world's oceans the water is given a cloudy, milky appearance by the billions of coccoliths that are gradually sinking to the bottom. The reader has probably guessed by now how Dorset's mighty chalk cliffs have been formed; when the rock is pure it is almost entirely from microscopic coccoliths that sank to the bottom of ancient oceans. There is, perhaps, no better way of appreciating geological time than to look at these chalk cliffs and imagine how long it must take for such tiny organisms to collect on the sea bed and be squeezed and compressed by ever increasing weight above into strong, resistant rock many hundreds of feet thick.

Looking west from Bat's Head

Durdle Door

Durdle Door is one of the most famous landmarks on the Jurassic Coast and has been photographed thousands of times. Made of Purbeck and Portland limestone, it is an erosional feature: the sea has exploited a weakness and widened a crack until eventually an arch has been formed large enough to sail a boat through. In time the arch will collapse leaving isolated rocks like those in neighbouring Man O'War Bay.

There are a number of reasons why planes of weakness or joints may develop in rocks. An obvious one is where different rocks meet, along a "bedding plane". At a number of places along the Jurassic Coast, hard limestone layers are interspersed among softer sandy or clay strata. At Durdle Door, however, the strata are aligned nearly vertically, folded and contorted by huge earth movements. These movements can cause weaknesses which are later widened by erosion. This is probably what has happened at Durdle Door.

Large planes of weakness where movement has occurred are known as faults. If the strata have been folded and tipped vertical it is not surprising that cracks and splits are also a feature. Faults are often obvious because they are picked out by streams or because soft rocks have been displaced against harder rocks, producing a noticeable "step" in the landscape.

At Durdle Door the soft Cretaceous rocks from the Wealden series between the Purbeck limestones and Chalk are much thinner than elsewhere. Think of Swanage Bay which has been carved out of these soft rocks between the Chalk and the limestones. At Durdle Door they have been almost squeezed out by folding and faulting. The actual picture is very complicated but this is partly due to a rather obvious fact. Under the tremendous pressures that caused these giant earth movements, different types of rock behave differently. Geologists talk of "competent" and "incompetent" strata. The hard chalk and limestones are competent and tend to retain their shape when folded whereas the soft clays and sands of the Wealden Beds do not.

Goats overlooking Durdle Door!

Durdle Door at dusk

Lulworth Cove

SY 828798

Visit Lulworth Cove on any day not in the school holidays and you will be unlucky not to see a group of youngsters on a school or college field trip. Lulworth is one of the British Isles' classic locations to study geology and physical geography.

On a very basic level the almost circular shape of the cove is easily explained by the sea breaching the harder Purbeck and Portland limestones and scouring away the softer Wealden sediments behind, before coming up against another hard rock at the back, chalk. The same process is happening at Stair Hole just west of the cove, although at a much earlier stage. While this explanation satisfies many visitors, others will no doubt be eager to learn about the actual mechanisms by which the sea erodes rocks; the effect of hydraulic pressures in joints for instance. But why are these sediments of such different hardness in the first place? Why do some deposits form hard, compact layers strong enough to build cathedrals while others crumble in the hand?

The answer lies with many factors, but chemistry and the starting materials are perhaps the two biggest. The Wealden deposits are mostly sands and clays deposited in river estuaries. As more and more sediment collects so the underlying layers are squeezed and compacted. Water is squeezed out and clay minerals tend to stick together, giving the newly formed rock some coherence. Sand grains do not stick together well and the sands in the Wealden are often very crumbly. However, for a rock to be really hard it needs a cement to stick the particles together. In limestones this is provided by calcium carbonate from shell creatures, dissolved in the seawater then precipitated out as the sediment is being compressed. We know that in the lagoons and oceans in which the Purbeck and Portland rocks formed such life abounded; that is where the calcium carbonate came from and why the Purbeck and Portland rocks are hard.

Finally, before leaving Lulworth, mention must be made of the Fossil Forest in the cliffs just past the eastern end of the cove. Here we can see fossilised tree stumps, 140 million years old, which were colonised by algal growths known as stromatolites. These trees were once in the Jurassic swamps where dinosaurs roamed. It is thought a sudden change in conditions, a rise in the water level, killed the trees and led to their colonisation by algae.

Lulworth Cove

Worbarrow Bay

SY 866805

Many of the fossil rich Jurassic clays of the Dorset coast were deposited in relatively deep seas, although land was never far away. As the continents continue their slow progress across the face of the Earth, so the pattern of land and sea continually changes. Towards the end of the Jurassic period much of what is now Dorset was covered by freshwater lagoons on the fringe of a landmass to the north and west. In these hot, swampy marshlands dinosaurs roamed while the onset of dry periods sometimes left their gigantic footprints for us to marvel at.

The start of the Cretaceous period saw conditions change again; this is obvious from the distinct change in the type of rocks we see. Worbarrow Bay is clearly carved out of very different sediments from those that form its southern and northern edges. Resistant limestones make up its southern flank while to the north the hard Chalk provides a formidable barrier. In between the rocks are conspicuously softer, producing crumbly cliffs and a gentle valley that winds its way back to the deserted village of Tyneham. It is the same picture at Swanage but here the strata have narrowed to a much homelier bay.

These softer rocks comprise the Wealden Series, sands and clays that formed in a large ancient river delta. Geologists have deduced this not only from the type of rock but also from the fossil record; for in these strata we find the remains of plants and creatures, that from living relatives, we know lived in freshwater. These Wealden deposits extend across southern England [taking their name from the Weald in Kent where they are most completely exposed] into France and Germany. It must have been a mighty river, although it has been speculated that the delta was not of the same order of size as that of the modern Ganges.

Gradually the sea encroached on the delta and we see marine sediments once more at the northern end of Worbarrow Bay culminating in the Chalk, a sediment almost wholly composed of microscopic marine life.

Worbarrow Bay

Worbarrow Bay from Flower's Barrow

Kimmeridge

SY 908792

It might be surprising to the summer visitor to this peaceful, un-commercialised bay that Kimmeridge has a long industrial heritage. The hard, black oil shale was mined by the Romans who turned and polished it into fashionable jewellery. Then in the 16th century a harbour was built to export the alum found in the shale. Alum, or hydrated potassium aluminium sulphate, was valuable as a fixer for the dyes used in the wool industry. Unfortunately the trade failed to develop. A French company then tried to export lamp oil made from the oil shale, but this too failed, possibly due to the unpleasant smell produced by the burning oil – although it surely must have been better than tallow candles! Finally, in the modern era, Kimmeridge has become a site of oil production, its small well with the famous "nodding donkey", once produced around 350 barrels per day. Note that the oil does not come from the oil shale exposed at Kimmeridge, but from earlier and deeper Jurassic strata. However, the Kimmeridge Clay is the source rock for the North Sea oil where it is buried deep underground. It has a high organic content, around 3.8% at Kimmeridge, which possibly indicates a sea bed lacking in oxygen.

Like Portland, Purbeck and Bridport, Kimmeridge has given its name to geological strata. Geologists refer to this part of the coast as the "type" location for the Kimmeridge Clay, indicating that it is well displayed here and has been studied extensively. These studies have given us much information about the conditions under which the sediments were deposited and then turned to rock. Looking at the cliffs you will see that soft bands of clay alternate with harder bands of shale. There seems to be some sort of repeating pattern here and that is what geologists have long been trying to understand. If there is a repeating pattern or cyclicity, then clearly the environment at the time of deposition must have changed in a cyclical or rhythmical way. The Kimmeridge Clay formation is around 500m thick, but when you allow for the sediment being compacted by the weight above, there must originally have been about 1250m of sediment. Geologists have estimated the deposition rate here to have been about 25cm per thousand years. Putting all these facts together with other evidence has led some to speculate that the rhythmical sedimentation may have been due to the changes in the tilt in the Earth's axis or obliquity. This in turn would have led to rhythmical climatic change which could account for the different sediments at different times of the cycle.

Kimmeridge Bay and Clavell Tower

Chapman's Pool

SY 958769

Chapman's Pool is a pretty bay sheltering between St. Aldhelm's Head and Houns-tout cliff to the west. It is difficult to get to as the descents from either side are steep and frequently slippery. In bad weather it can present as a grey, forbidding place.

Like some other cliffs on the Jurassic Coast, Houns-tout owes its height to a capping of hard rocks, here the limestones of the Portland Series. Underneath, the soft Kimmeridge Clays of the Upper Jurassic are clearly less durable: extensive landslides testify to this. The lovely Encombe Valley also reflects the geology; cut into the soft clays by a stream while behind the spur of Swyre Head is a branch of the Purbeck limestone uplands that itself was once a coastal headland.

Chapman's Pool is a favourite with fossil hunters; ammonites are common in the dark clays, in particular the large and attractive specimen known as *Pavlovia rotunda*. The fossils here are often crushed and fragile. Remember, when large thicknesses of fine sediment collect on the sea floor huge pressures are involved.

Chapman's Pool is a good place for appreciating how geologists build up a picture of past events – geological history. The rocks of Houns-tout are from the Upper Jurassic. Notice how they change from the bottom to the top of the cliff. Dark grey clays merge into lighter coloured clays and sands, followed by hard limestones. These changing rock types represent changing conditions in the Jurassic oceans, changing depth and proximity to land. The lighter coloured rocks near the top of the cliff are known as the Portland Sands, although they are mostly clays or marls. Marls are clay sediments with a high content of calcium carbonate. Today we know that calcium carbonate can be precipitated in the ocean where there are large numbers of photosynthesising algae. Perhaps these Jurassic marls were formed in a warm, shallow algae rich ocean. Later on at the end of the Jurassic the Purbeck Limestones were formed in shallow, fresh-water lagoons.

View from St. Aldhelm's Head

Looking west over Chapman's Pool

Seacombe

Limestone is a sediment with a high proportion of the mineral calcium carbonate. You may remember that a simple test for this is to put a drop of dilute hydrochloric acid on it and watch it fizz. The calcium carbonate in limestones has been manufactured by living organisms that have extracted the required elements from seawater and used it to make themselves hard parts, typically outer shells for protection. Thus limestones are indicative of a marine environment rich in life, often forming in shallow, warm, tropical seas. Some limestones contain a high proportion of broken shell material whilst others consist of calcium carbonate that has precipitated out of sea water rich in the substance because shells and other carbonate hard parts have previously been dissolved.

The Portland Stone at Seacombe is of the latter variety and is known as an oolitic limestone. The name is descriptive, coming from the Greek word for an egg; the stone consists of millions of tiny ooliths, spherical grains of calcium carbonate that precipitated around even more tiny shell fragments or sand grains as they were rolled gently around the sea floor by currents in shallow, tropical water. Such a location today may be found off the Bahamas.

Look closely at a fragment of the rock and you should just be able to see the spherical ooliths bound together by a calcium carbonate cement. When such sedimentation is allowed to continue without interruption or disturbance for many thousands, even millions of years, the result is a strong, homogeneous rock that is an excellent building stone. This is what we have here at Seacombe.

You might notice that the broad uniform layers of the Portland Stone are sometimes broken by layers of chert nodules. Chert is micro-crystalline silica, the dark grey-black variety is known as flint. Chemically the same as quartz, it is composed of the two most abundant elements in the Earth's crust, silicon and oxygen. Stone Age man used it for tools, aware of its hard nature and the fact that it broke along curved surfaces, enabling it to be shaped into effective axe and arrow heads. Some creatures, typically microscopic, use it for their hard protective parts. When they die the silica can again be dissolved, sometimes leading to high concentrations. As the layers of sediment are compressed by the increasing weight of sediment on top, the silica can be precipitated out, forming the chert nodules we see today.

The Portland Stone at Seacombe

Handfast Point

Handfast Point overlooking Studland Bay is a good place for the Jurassic Coast to end. Even to the uninitiated it is clear the structure of the landscape changes dramatically beyond this point. Look north from the Chalk cliffs and you see the vast Hampshire Basin stretching out before you, the expanse of Poole Harbour, sandy heathlands and the crumbling sandy cliffs of Bournemouth and its neighbouring holiday resorts.

The Upper Cretaceous period had seen the spread of the Chalk Sea; much of Britain was inundated and as we have seen, the lack of sediment derived from land has led geologists to speculate that the Chalk Sea was surrounded by a waterless desert. The end of the Cretaceous period, and the whole geological era defined by the Triassic, Jurassic and Cretaceous, is marked by the withdrawal of the Chalk Sea, indicating earth movements on a grand scale. Much of Britain now became land and a long period of erosion followed. Great thicknesses of the "newly" formed Chalk were removed, in some areas as much as 500 feet. Eventually further earth movements led to the return of the sea and sediments were deposited in several large synclines [down folds] or "basins" such as the Hampshire Basin we see before us. These sediments rest unconformably on the Chalk, although the difference in dip of the strata is very slight.

It is time to remind ourselves that the end of the Cretaceous is not defined by these great geographical changes but by changes in the fossil record. At the end of the Cretaceous there took place another mass extinction of plant and animal species. Around 85% of all living species died out in this calamitous event about 65 million years ago. Casualties included the dinosaurs and ammonites, and intriguingly, it seems that all large land animals became extinct. The most likely cause is presently thought to be the impact of a giant asteroid or meteorite.

Look carefully at the famous sea stacks of Old Harry and his family and you will notice the well-defined horizontal bedding planes of the Chalk. Elsewhere on the Chalk ridge that bounds the Isle of Purbeck you may be aware that the Chalk dips steeply. The same is true of the Chalk on the northern edge of Swanage Bay. Somewhere in between Swanage and Handfast Point a large fault has brought the horizontal limb of the giant fold in the Chalk up against the near vertical part.

Old Harry and his family at Handfast Point

Fossils

There is something uniquely exciting about finding a fossil. There, in your hand, is the perfect spiral of an ammonite that lived, perhaps, 100 million years ago in a tropical ocean where you are now standing. Imagine the sequence of events that has led to this small creature being discovered now by you.

As most people know, fossils are the remains of living things that died long ago and have somehow come to be preserved in rocks. They can take many forms. Sometimes actual shells or bones are preserved while sometimes just a cast or mould of the creature is left. Naturally it is almost always the hard parts that are preserved or that leave an impression. Occasionally it is the trace of an animal that survives, for example a dinosaur footprint or the burrow of a worm. We have all seen in shops ammonites that look as if they are made of gold; in fact "fools' gold" or iron pyrites. This has formed as the sediment is being squeezed and compacted. The original shell has been dissolved away and a replacement mineral precipitated in its place, often miraculously preserving even the minutest detail.

Fossils are useful in many ways. Clearly they document the evolution of life on Earth and with increasing sophistication of scientific instruments we are able to detect the remains of microscopic creatures that existed thousands of millions of years ago. They also help geologists to correlate rock strata from different locations. Rocks form in many different environments and by identifying, say, a limestone in one location as the same age as a sandstone in another we are able to build a picture of ancient geographies. It has long been recognised that each period of time has a unique assemblage of fossils, since species are continually evolving and dying out. Some animals, such as the ammonites, help us by evolving very quickly and so give us very precise time markers. As we have seen before it is the fossil record that is used to define periods and eras of geological time. We should also be aware that fossils do not give us absolute timings, only relative. Absolute dates are only obtained by radio-isotope dating, a technique that the Victorian pioneers of geology did not have!

Opposite: The remains of an ammonite on Monmouth Beach, Lyme Regis, showing the internal chambered structure.

The Geological Time Scale

Era	Period		Age[my]
Cenozoic	Quaternary	Neogene	25
		Palaeogene	65
Mesozoic	Cretaceous		145
	Jurassic		200
	Triassic		250
Palaeozoic	Permian		300
	Carboniferous		360
	Devonian		415
	Silurian		445
	Ordovician		490
	Cambrian		550
Pre-Cambrian			4600

Further Reading:

The Official Guide to the Jurassic Coast - *edited by Professor Denys Brunsden*
The Geology of the Jurassic Coast: The Red Coast Revealed, Exmouth to Lyme Regis - *by Richard Edwards*
Fossils and Rocks of the Jurassic Coast - *by Robert Westwood*

Some useful websites:

www.jurassiccoast.com - the official website of the Jurassic Coast Trust
www.soton.ac.uk/~imw/ - "Geology of the Wessex Coast of Southern England" by Dr. Ian West. A very detailed and comprehensive guide for serious students.
www.geolsoc.org.uk - some general on-line resources from the Geologists Association
www.discoveringfossils.co.uk - lots of general information
www.naturalengland.org.uk - Search for "England's geology" for a county by county guide.

Maps - OS Explorer series 115,116 & OL15